DISNEY · PIXAR

Cars 2

Top Secret Missions

PaRragon

Bath · New York · Singapore · Hong Kong · Cologne · Delhi
Melbourne · Amsterdam · Johannesburg · Auckland · Shenzhen

First published by Parragon in 2011

Parragon
Queen Street House
4 Queen Street
Bath BA1 1HE, UK

ISBN 978-1-4454-2081-3

Printed in China.

This book belongs to:

Davi

From; Ms Lopes

CONTENTS

My True Identity

Record your true identity details on this page. Remember this is for *your eyes only*.

My real name:

My real age:

My hometown:

When I'm not spying, I like to:

Use an inkpad and print your thumbprint here:

My Secret Agent Identity

Every secret agent needs a false identity.
Record your *secret agent* details on this page.

My secret name:

My preferred disguise:

My secret agent age:

My secret agent hometown:

**The password I use to unlock
top-secret files:**

I'm a Secret Agent!

The secret agents in *Cars 2* are quick, intelligent, and have tons of cool gadgets. If you were a spy car, what would you be like?

What gadgets would you have?

What unique talents would you have?

What color would you be?

Would you work alone or with associate agents?

Draw yourself as a super-spy car!

Secret *Cars 2* Profiles

Finn McMissile

Finn McMissile is a super secret agent! He is quick, sly, and brave. He is a fearsome fighter who always comes to the rescue and defeats the bad guys. His many spy gadgets mean he is prepared for any situation, including turning into a submarine!

Holley Shiftwell

Holley is new to the spy game, but that doesn't stop her. She uses her special talents to trick her enemies and create clever disguises. She can even fly!

Mater

Mater is an old, rusty tow truck from Radiator Springs, but when he gets mistaken for an American intelligence agent he has to whip into action! His ability to drive backward, his knowledge of mechanics, and his happy-go-lucky attitude make him an excellent spy, even though he's always getting into trouble. He is Lightning's best friend.

Lightning McQueen

Lightning started out as a rookie race car with dreams of living life in the fast lane. He is now a three-time Piston Cup champion, but has learned there's more to life than winning.

13

Cool Coloring

Finn McMissile is on an important mission.
Color him in.

Cool Coloring

Color tow truck Mater. He's a secret agent!

My Secret Journal

What did you do as a super secret agent today?

Today I went on a secret mission to . . .

I went with . . .

While we were there we saw . . .

We had to save . . .

from . . .

The name of the bad guy was . . .

We celebrated our victory by . . .

My next secret mission is . . .

My Espionage Team

Great secret agents need associates to help them on secret missions. Who are your spy friends? Fill out their details and add photographs too.

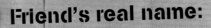

Friend's real name:

Friend's spy name:

Secret gadget:

Friend's real name:

Friend's spy name:

Secret gadget:

Friend's real name:

Friend's spy name:

Secret gadget:

Friend's real name:

Friend's spy name:

Secret gadget:

Espionage Team Code

Now that you have your team together, create a secret code so that you can send messages to each other without the enemy knowing!

Choose a different letter, a number, or a symbol to represent each letter of the alphabet.

A B C D E F G H I J K L M
_ _ _ _ _ _ _ _ _ _ _ _ _

N O P Q R S T U V W X Y Z
_ _ _ _ _ _ _ _ _ _ _ _ _

Mater's Maze

Mater has been trapped by the Lemons. Help Finn rescue him, but make sure you avoid the bad guys!

Wordsearch

How much espionage training do you have? See how many pieces of information you can decipher in this wordsearch. Find the words in the list.

S	E	C	R	E	T	M	G	N	U	I	L	N
J	A	G	E	N	T	Q	E	F	N	P	W	O
M	C	C	T	O	A	K	A	P	C	E	M	I
L	W	Y	D	M	R	Y	O	N	U	G	I	T
E	C	N	E	G	I	L	L	E	T	N	I	A
K	X	L	Q	M	T	I	K	L	E	Y	F	G
X	O	Y	W	S	I	E	X	F	T	V	Z	I
X	V	H	C	N	P	S	G	B	X	I	V	T
D	J	G	Y	L	C	R	S	D	T	G	N	S
L	R	E	S	C	U	E	J	I	A	B	R	E
D	Q	W	G	X	N	C	N	F	O	G	K	V
S	G	E	S	I	U	G	S	I	D	N	A	N
I	L	H	T	P	H	L	S	O	J	Y	F	I

GADGET

DISGUISE

SECRET

MISSION

AGENT

INTELLIGENCE

INVESTIGATION

RESCUE

Spy the Difference

Finn McMissile is a super-cool government agent. He has gadgets galore! Spot 5 differences between these two pictures.

Top Secret Pages

Write down all the secret missions you would like to go on here, then seal the pages with invisible tape so no one can find your secret agent secrets!

I would like to go to:

I would like to go with:

One piece of classified information I have never shared is:

My biggest secret is:

Something I only do in secret is:

The only fellow agent I trust with my secrets is:

A space for confidential information that you don't want anyone to see!

International Travel

Secret agents have to travel all over the globe on important missions. Where would you go?

I would like to go to ....

This is a picture of me on a secret mission there.

I would like to go to ....

This is a picture of me on a secret mission there.

Cool Coloring

Color this awesome picture of Francesco.
He's a famous Italian racer.

Cool Coloring

Color this picture of Raoul ÇaRoule.
He's one of the best rally cars.

Espionage Training

Secret agents have to be very clever. Fill in your favorite things about school on these pages.

The subject I am best at is:

My favorite subject is:

. . . because:

My least favorite subject is:

. . . because:

My favorite teacher is:

. . . because:

When I'm older I want to be:

. . . because:

A Secret Agent Party

Impress your friends with a super-cool secret agent party. Get planning on this page!

These are the people I will invite:

The dress code will be:

The games we'll play will be:

This is the food we'll eat:

Espionage Party Game

Find lots of clothes that could be used as secret agent disguises—such as hats, wigs, trench coats, glasses, and fake moustaches—and divide them into two piles. Split your friends into two teams for a relay race.

Each person in turn must put on a disguise, run to one end of the room and back, then let the next person go.

The first team to finish wins!

Photographic Evidence

Use these pages to keep photos and mementos from your spy missions with your friends!

This was our most exciting mission!

This was
our most
dangerous
mission!

Who's Who?

A good secret agent has an excellent eye for detail. Can you tell which characters are in these close ups?

A.

B.

A. Finn McMissile B. Francesco Bernoulli C. Holley Shiftwell D. Mater E. Lightning McQueen

C.

D.

E.

Save Lightning!

Secret Agent Mater needs to get to the race to save his best friend Lightning McQueen. Get him through the maze quickly before the bomb goes off!

Crack the Code

Which Italian race car beats Lightning to the finish line in Japan? Crack the code to find out!

O A C

R E F N S

– – – – – – – – –

Super Squares

This is a game for two secret agents. Take it in turns to draw a line between two dots. If your line completes a square, write your initials inside it. When all the dots are full, count up your squares and the player with the most wins!

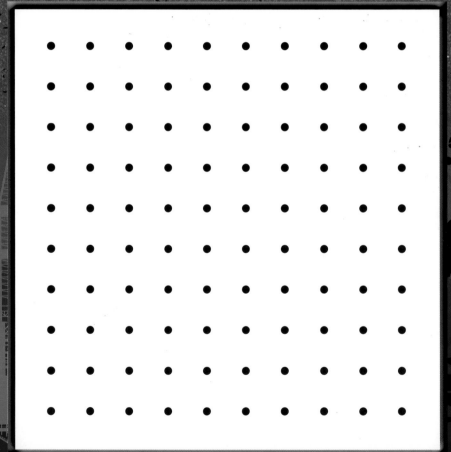

Cool Coloring

Color this awesome picture of Lightning McQueen.

The Finish Line

My favorite page in this book was:

The most difficult page to complete was:

My favorite *Cars 2* character is:

My next secret mission will be:

I finished this book on:

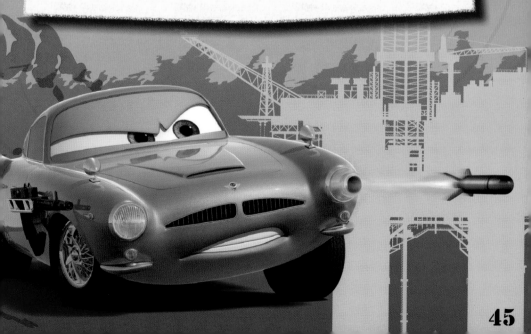

45